BATTLE BOOKS

HASTINGS

Gary Smailes

Illustrated by Ollie Cuthbertson

For Jacob —— G.S.

First published in 2011
by Franklin Watts

Text © Gary Smailes 2011
Illustrations © Ollie Cuthbertson 2011
Cover design by Jonathan Hair

Franklin Watts
338 Euston Road
London NW1 3BH

Franklin Watts Australia
Level 17/207 Kent Street
Sydney, NSW 2000

A CIP catalogue record for this book
is available from the British Library.

ISBN: 978 1 4451 0112 5

1 3 5 7 9 10 8 6 4 2

Printed in Great Britain

Franklin Watts is a division of Hachette Children's Books,
an Hachette UK company.
www.hachette.co.uk

"When I went to school my history lessons were all about learning the names of kings and endless lists of dates. *Yawn*. But exciting history asks: How did people live and how did they die? How did they feel? Were they just like us or more like aliens from another planet? Those are the questions that *Battle Books* explore. I wish Gary Smailes and his books had been around when I went to school."
— **Terry Deary, author of *Horrible Histories***

BATTLE BOOKS

Prepare to fight your own battle...

Fight your own battle by starting the story, then choosing which numbered paragraph to follow. Go to that paragraph to continue on and see if you can gain a "great general ranking" and defeat the English at the Battle of Hastings!

William the Conqueror

This is YOU – the Duke of Normandy and the rightful King of England. You command the biggest army ever seen and have the support of the Pope – leader of the Catholic Church. You are a mighty warrior who can fight on either horseback or foot.

◊ Country: Normandy
◊ Fighting ability: Superb
◊ Armour: Chainmail
◊ Troop type: Cavalry
◊ Favourite weapon: Any!

YOUR LEADERS

Eustace III

Eustace is the Count of Boulogne, leader of the French and as powerful as William the Conqueror. He is William's rival but has chosen to fight on the Norman side in order to ensure Harold is removed from the English throne. He is a mighty warrior who can fight on either horseback or foot.
◊ Country: France
◊ Troop type: Cavalry
◊ Fighting ability: Superb
◊ Favourite weapon: Broadsword
◊ Armour: Chainmail

Odo of Bayeux

He is the trusted half-brother of William the Conqueror and is the Bishop of Bayeux in Normandy. Odo is not a knight and prefers to direct the battle rather then get caught up fighting. If forced to fight Odo prefers to remain on his horse.
◊ Country: Normandy
◊ Troop type: Cavalry
◊ Fighting ability: Poor
◊ Favourite weapon: Mace
◊ Armour: Chainmail

YOUR TROOPS

William's Infantry

These are well trained warriors who fight on foot. They are armed with spears and swords and are protected by shields, steel helmets and chainmail.
◊ Country: Normandy, Breton and France
◊ Troop type: Infantry
◊ Fighting ability: Good
◊ Favourite weapon: Spear and sword
◊ Armour: Chainmail

William's Archers

Mostly peasants, these troops try to avoid getting involved in hand to hand combat. They are armed with bows and prefer to do their killing from a distance. They may have a dagger to protect themselves but very few have any armour.
◊ Country: Normandy, Breton and France
◊ Troop type: Infantry
◊ Fighting ability: Poor
◊ Favourite weapon: Bow
◊ Armour: None

Alan IV

Alan Fergant is the Duke of Brittany and leader of the Bretons. The Bretons recently fought a war with the Normans but have now become friends to fight the English. Alan Fergant is a knight who prefers to fight on horseback.
◊ Country: Brittany
◊ Troop type: Cavalry
◊ Fighting ability: Good
◊ Favourite weapon: Lance
◊ Armour: Chainmail

William's Knights

These are the most feared troops in William's army. They are well trained and capable of carrying out complex moves in small groups. They are mounted on mighty warhorses and fight with lances. They are protected by shields, steel helmets and chainmail.
◊ Country: Normandy, Breton and France
◊ Troop type: Cavalry
◊ Fighting ability: Good
◊ Favourite weapon: Lance
◊ Armour: Chainmail

ENGLISH LEADERS

Harold II

Harold Godwinson is the leader of the English army and the crowned King of England. His army recently defeated the Viking king Harald Hardrade at the Battle of Stamford Bridge and he has marched across England to fight this battle. Harold prefers to fight on foot.
◊ Country: England
◊ Troop type: Infantry
◊ Fighting ability: Superb
◊ Favourite weapon: Broadsword
◊ Armour: Chainmail

TROOPS

Fyrds

These are English warriors. They come from all parts of the country and many are not trained to fight. Some may be noblemen, whilst others are simple farmers. They have all kinds of weapons and armour, though most fight with spears. They fight on foot and specialise in the shield wall formation.
◊ Country: England
◊ Troop type: Infantry
◊ Fighting ability: Poor
◊ Favourite weapon: Spear
◊ Armour: Leather

Housecarls

These are the personal body guard of King Harold and will fight to the death to protect him. Some are armed with spears and swords but the most feared wield huge two handed axes that can cut a man in half. They fight on foot.
◊ Country: England
◊ Troop type: Infantry
◊ Fighting ability: Superb
◊ Favourite weapon: Axe
◊ Armour: Chainmail

It is a cold autumn morning in 1066 and you stand on an English hill waiting to do battle with Harold Godwinson, the King of England. You recently sailed from your home in France with a massive fleet of ships, filled with the best warriors from Normandy, Breton and France. The traitor Harold has defied God by declaring himself King of England and you have come to claim your rightful place as king. You and your army intend to settle this matter today at what will become known as the Battle of Hastings.

In the valley ahead, your mighty army prepares for battle. Mounted knights keep a tight rein on their huge horses, infantry march in groups with their massive kite shields protecting their bodies and deadly archers prepare for action.

POSITIONS AT THE START OF THE BATTLE OF HASTINGS

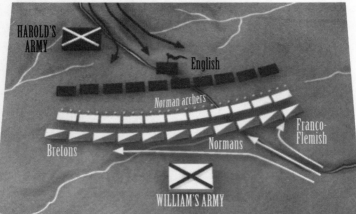

Your archers are strung out in a thin line in front of your army and behind them are three groups of warriors. On the left are the Bretons commanded by Alan Fergant, in the centre are the Normans who will be under your command, with the help of your half-brother Bishop Odo, and on the right are the French under the instruction of Eustace of Boulogne.

In each of the three groups there are both infantry and cavalry. The infantry fight on foot and are armed with spears and protected by chainmail, steel helmets and large shields. The cavalry are mounted on warhorses and the riders are also protected by chainmail, helmets and shields, but instead they fight with short spears, called lances.

On the hill opposite waits the English army. Harold has chosen to defend the hill top and his infantry have taken position on the lip of the hill. They are in a formation called a shield wall – in which the shields of the front rank touch together.

You know that if you are to win this battle then you must break this wall. Now move quickly to section 1 before the battle begins without you…

1 The early morning sun is low in the sky and its rays feel warm on your face. You are mounted on your favourite warhorse down in the valley, positioning yourself on a small mound just behind your army.

Your army is huge and you have to turn your head from left to right to take in the whole mass of men. It contains more than 7,000 warriors and would be impossible for you to control alone. The commanders that will carry your orders are mounted on warhorses too. Your half-brother Odo, a bishop and knight, is at your side. Alan Fergant is on the left in charge of the Bretons and Eustace is away to your right with his French troops.

Your thoughts are broken by the voice of your trusted friend Ivo Taillefer. He is dressed in chainmail armour, carries a lance and rides a large white horse.

"Sire, I wish to be the first to strike a blow against the English. Let me charge alone ahead of your mighty army and teach the English pigs what it means to cross swords with a true Norman knight."

◊ *If you wish to let Ivo charge the English, go to 56.*
◊ *If you feel Ivo's request is suicide, then go to 83.*

The housecarl's axe whistles through the air. You remain calm and duck at the last moment. The blade misses your head and smashes into your shoulder. Your armour deflects it, but you are stunned and unable to react. You squeeze your eyes shut and wait for the blow that will end your life…but it never comes.

You regain your senses, flicking open your eyes. The housecarl is surrounded by your knights. Their lances have speared his body. You recover quickly from the attack, leaping back on to your horse, but control of the battle is slipping away.

Many of the English have fled, but two groups remain. To the right, about 500 housecarls have grouped together. However, about 1,000 of your Norman warriors have organised themselves to fight against them. Your attention falls on the centre of the hill top, where about 30 housecarls are defending the body of their dead king. You suspect these are Harold's personal bodyguard.

The only men you have to command are your bodyguard. The Norman infantry and cavalry are engaged with the housecarls. Eustace's French warriors are chasing English fyrds from the battlefield. Alan Fergant is nowhere to be seen.

◊ *To send your knights to kill the English warriors protecting Harold's body, go to 47.*

◊ *If you wish to let them live, go to 53.*

3 You stand, motionless, watching the battle unfold on the lip of the hill. Suddenly you see Odo riding away from you, heading for the cavalry. He is talking to the cavalry. He has ignored you and is telling them to prepare to attack. You are furious!

◊ *Go to 72.*

4 Even though Odo and Eustace are close, you begin to realise that the situation is beyond your control as the retreating crowd gets larger.

Panic sweeps through you. You jump from your horse and race into the crowd. Many warriors are rushing past you, some even banging into you as they desperately try to escape. You scream at the men to stop but they ignore you.

The battle is lost – there is nothing else you can do for your men. All you can do now is hope that you can escape alive.

◊ *For you the Battle of Hastings is over. Go to 11 to discover your fate.*

You suddenly feel very tired and the will to continue the fight slips from your body. You have clearly defeated the English, and with the English king dead, the throne is yours for the taking.

You pass the order to the nearby troops to end the fighting. The path back to your tent is strewn with the bodies and limbs of dead soldiers. You emerge from the trees. The sun is low in the sky and all about the battlefield dead and dying warriors lay unattended.

You pass some of your men slumped to the ground, their exhausted bodies desperate for rest. Others are making small fires to cook food, or searching through the bodies of the dead looking for valuable items.

The day has been hard, yet though your heart is heavy with grief, you know that you are one step closer to being the King of England.

◊ *Congratulations…you have defeated the English. However, your victory is not complete. Go to 71 to discover your fate.*

You quickly issue orders to Odo and Eustace to stop the retreating army. Your commanders disappear from view. For a moment you relax, happy that they are rallying their men. But as you watch, hundreds of your men stream down from the hillside and head back along the road that they had travelled earlier that morning. They are desperately heading for the coast and the safety of your fort at Pevensey. The English army know that you are beaten! They have pushed forward from the slope and are now either fighting hard in the valley, or chasing your fleeing men.

Panic sweeps through your body. The battle is lost – there is nothing else you can do for your men – you must now escape.

◊ *For you the Battle of Hastings is over. Go to 11 to discover your fate.*

---

7   It takes some time for your army to prepare for battle. Eventually, you see that the men have lined up as before. Alan Fergant and his Breton warriors are on the left, the Normans in the centre and the French, under Eustace, on the right. The infantry are in the front ranks and the knights are behind. You have no arrows left, so you have ordered the archers off the battlefield.

The battle is proving more difficult than you ever imagined. The English shield wall seems unbreakable, and you know you must try something different. You turn to Odo and explain that the time is right for a feint attack. The knights should charge forward, then once in combat, pull back and lure the fyrds out.

Odo looks confused. "Brother, the fyrds may be

undisciplined but Harold is not stupid. If we send
the cavalry forward straight away he will suspect
something is wrong. It is God's will that we attack
with the infantry first. That way the English will
not suspect a trap."

◊ *To follow Odo's advice, you can order the infantry to*
  attack at 80.
◊ *If you feel Odo is being too careful, go to 17.*

Across the hill top, warriors from both sides are
engaged in battle. There are gaps where your men
have not yet attacked the shield wall, and it is here
that you order your Norman knights to attack.

About fifty horsemen gather at the base of the
slope, led by a knight carrying a flag with a dragon
on it. It is Ralf of Tosny.

The charge begins slowly but soon picks up
speed. The knights have not couched their lances
under their arms. Instead, they have them poised
high above their heads. The horsemen hurl the
lances into the English shield wall. Then, with
great skill, they pull their horses away before any
defenders can strike back. Many of the lances
bounce harmlessly off the shields and armour, but
some strike their targets resulting in screams of
agony and fountains of blood. You see flashes of
light in the autumn sun as the knights draw their
swords. The most skilful knights now pull close to

the wall and lean over the enemy shields, striking down onto the English.

The knights fight on and you shift nervously in your saddle, then finally Ralf breaks away, his dragon flag thrust high above his head. The knights follow and wheel away from the wall.

For the feint to work the English must follow. You know that the disciplined housecarls would never break from the strong shield wall, but the inexperienced fyrds might. At first, nothing happens. Then suddenly hundreds of fyrds stream down the hill after the knights.

Then as planned, Ralf of Tosny turns his horse sharply and brings his cavalry about, to face the charging fyrds. Without their shield wall to protect them, the English fyrds are cut down by the knights.

Your attention returns to the remaining English. King Harold has filled the gap behind the shield wall. Your feint may not have won the battle, but it has killed many English warriors and weakened the shield wall. What will you do next?

◊ *If you wish to order another feint attack, speed to 64.*
◊ *If you wish to wait and see if the English shield wall collapses, go to 50.*

9 From your position you can see hundreds of your infantry dying as arrows and stones thud into their bodies. The sight is too much and you pass the order for the infantry to retreat. The infantry are reluctant to move and it takes time for the retreat to begin.

Your broken men collect at the base of the hill. As you look, you see that many of them are shaking their heads and shouting words in your direction. The warriors are brave and proud men. To retreat in battle was an insult.

◊ *To order the infantry to attack again, go to 75.*

◊ *However, if you think the English can't be beaten, order an all-out retreat by going to 35.*

You signal for the strange man to speak. He bows and then speaks.

"Sire, I bring great news. My men have been toiling all day to bring our carts to the battlefield. Now we are here. What should I do with my arrows?"

Suddenly you remember. When you advanced this morning you were forced to leave behind the slow-moving carts that carried the supply of arrows. You had forgotten all about them, until now.

◊ *If you want the man to give out the arrows, go to 14.*
◊ *If you do not trust him, go to 27.*

Rating: Poor General

It all started so well, but ended up going very badly wrong. It is important that as a medieval general you are decisive and show real courage. It is also vital that you learn when to ignore your commanders and when to take their advice. Now learn from your mistakes and go back to section 1 to try again. Quick, while you still have the chance to prove yourself a great general...

You turn to your knights and bark out the order to attack, before racing to the head of the charge.

As you reach the bottom of the slope your sword is free and swinging. You are moving at pace and it is difficult to direct your horse into a gap in the mass of fighting warriors at the top of the slope. When you hit the weakened shield wall, your men are only a few paces behind you.

You kill an Englishman with ease, your sword slicing into his flesh, and another. Then you are in trouble. Your horse suddenly stops. The shift in weight throws you forward. You struggle to stay in the saddle as the horse rears its legs high in the air, kicking out. You are pushed backwards. This time you lose your balance and tumble over the rear of the horse. You hit the ground hard.

Blackness...

Silence...

Then...sound rushes back.

You open your eyes and see a small man with a ragged beard carrying a worn spear. In one motion he thrusts it down into your chest. You try to move but it is hopeless. As you lie on the English soil, your life blood flows from the wound. Your final thought is of your home in Normandy.

◊ *Your army has defeated the English. However, your death means your victory is not complete. Go to 71 to discover your fate.*

13 You know a battle can be won or lost by a single decision, and you pray you are doing the right thing. You have faith in your men. You also have confidence in your commanders. Convinced that you do not need to interfere in the battle on the slope, your mind turns to the fleeing left wing. You can see that many of the Bretons have stopped running. They have grouped together at the base of the hill. However, they are outnumbered and the English swarm around them, it will not be long before they are slaughtered. You must act now.

◊ *To risk your life and charge with your bodyguard to help the Bretons, then go quickly to 33.*

◊ *If you feel the Bretons can manage, go to 92.*

14 You scream at the man to pass out the arrows and it is not long before your archers reappear on the battlefield. They are poised at the base of the slope, awaiting your orders. You spur your horse towards the leader of the archers. The battle is in the balance and the skilful use of arrows could win the day.

◊ *If you wish to order your archers to shoot over the top of the fighting front rank into the English on the hill top behind, then go to 74.*

◊ *If you wish to order the arrows to be shot into the English shield wall, even though it is still fighting with your men, go to 52.*

You panic and order the cavalry to retreat. You watch silently as the knights begin to ride back down the slope. The retreat is met by a huge cheer from the English. Yet, the carnage is not over for the knights. As they turn from the English army, they expose their backs and you are forced to watch helplessly as hundreds of retreating knights are cut down and killed. Your poor decisions are costing unnecessary losses. What will you do next?

◊ *If you wish to order the cavalry to attack again, go to 20. However, if you feel the Battle of Hastings is already lost, then go to 35.*

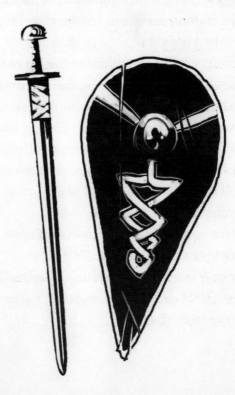

16 You decide that you have no choice but to risk your life and you urge your horse forward.

Objects are falling all around you – some striking your armour. You scream at your men, urging them to attack – but no one is listening. Then you realise you are not alone. Your half-brother Odo is next to you. He is also screaming at the men. Slowly, men rise to their feet and resume the attack as courage flows once again in their veins. You decide you can do no more, and return to safety at the centre of the army.

The infantry finally reach the top of the hill and a war cry of "Thor's aid" bellows out moments before the human wave hits. At first the English line is pushed back, but slowly the shield wall returns to its original position on the lip of the hill.

Desperately, each side thrust their weapons into the gaps between shields, stabbing and slashing at faces and arms. The fighting is bloody and desperate. Yet no matter how hard your men fight, the wall does not break. It is clear that the infantry alone will not smash the shield wall. You still have your cavalry waiting to attack.

◊ *If you feel now is the correct time, then order your knights to attack by going to 72.*

◊ *However, if you feel the attack has failed and a cavalry charge will not help, then order your infantry to retreat at 21.*

Though you respect your half-brother and his knowledge of battle tactics, you are sure that he is wrong. The English will not be expecting you to pretend to retreat and you feel certain they will fall for the trap. You firmly instruct Odo to get his men ready for the charge. You take the chance to examine the English army. They stretch out across the lip of the hill, their shields interlocked in the shield wall.

Movement in the valley draws your attention away from the hill. A small group of about fifty Norman cavalry have collected at the base of the slope. Though Odo is directing the horsemen, another knight is unmistakably in charge. You recognise a flag, with a dragon on, as that of Ralf of Tosny. Suddenly the small group of knights spring forward and surge up the hill. Almost immediately you realise your mistake.

As soon as the horses are within range, a black cloud of missiles arches into the air, over the ranks of the English and smashes into your knights. The effect of the attack is devastating and the air is filled with the cries of your injured warriors. The attack is too much for your brave knights, and they turn away and head back down the slope.

Your half-brother Odo reappears by your side and suggests you send the infantry forward to try to break the shield wall.

◊ *If you wish to follow Odo's advice, go to 48.*
◊ *If you wish to ignore Odo and send the cavalry forward for a second attack, move now to 28.*

Your men have risked their lives many times and
still the battle is far from won. However, you feel
that you must order another attack. You look about
and command a nearby knight to find Odo and
Eustace. He disappears without a word. Warriors
on both sides are sitting down. Some have set up
small fires and brewed up drinks, whilst others lie
on the floor seemingly asleep.

Within a few minutes, Odo and Eustace ride
over to you. The presence of your commanders
makes you feel safe. You explain that you wish
to order another attack, but neither of your
commanders answer. The battle has reached a lull
and for a moment all you can hear is the singing of
the birds in the distance. At last, your half-brother
Odo breaks the silence.

"Are you sure that you wish your men to attack
so soon? They are tired and in need of rest."

◊ *If you wish to ignore Odo's words and issue the order
to attack, then go to 61.*

◊ *However, if you feel Odo is correct and you wish to
let your men rest, then go to 89.*

19 You demand that the man finds your archers and passes out the arrows. The little man walks away quickly without another word.

Soon you see many peasants scuttling about the battlefield with rolls of arrows tucked under their arms. It is not long before your archers reappear on the battlefield and make their way to the front to await your orders.

You spur your horse towards the commander of the archers.

◊ *If you wish to order your archers to shoot over the top of the fighting front rank into the English on the hill top behind, then go to 74.*

◊ *If you wish to order the arrows to be shot into the English shield wall, even though it is still fighting with your men, go to 76.*

---

20 Though your cavalry have been battered, you judge that they are still ready to fight. You pass the word for your knights to attack again.

At last the cavalry spring forward and thunder up the slope. At first the charge is frantic, but the slope gets steeper and your men slow down. As the knights edge closer to the English line, a mass of missiles arc over the ranks of the English and into the charging horses.

The torrent of missiles is unending, and the cavalry attack grinds to a halt. The knights pause

in confusion and then turn to retreat down the
slope again.

◊ *Will you risk your life by riding forward to prevent
the retreat? If so, go to 24.*

◊ *Alternatively, you can order all of your men to
retreat by going to 43.*

At this moment the battle seems lost. Your infantry
are fighting for their lives, and though they are
showing great skill and courage, the English shield
wall looks as though it will never break. You
decide that your men are dying with no gain. You
call your half-brother Odo to your side and explain
that the men must retreat. He looks surprised and
then gently explains.

"Sire, the men are fighting for their lives. Even
if we wanted them to retreat, they would not hear
the order."

◊ *If you feel you have no option but to order your
cavalry to attack, go to 72.*

◊ *If you wish to wait and see what happens, go to 3.*

You decide that you must show your men that you are still alive. Your helmet is tied with a leather cord that runs under your chin. Your hands are sticky with English blood and it is difficult to untie the knot. You pull a dagger from your belt and slice through the leather cord to free the helmet.

Eustace of Boulogne is still at your side and you both ride forward at a slow pace. You lift the helmet from your face. Eustace is shouting and waving his flag, pointing in your direction. Slowly, the retreating warriors turn and see you. Delight and relief bursts across their faces. The word quickly spreads – you are alive!

You raise yourself high in your saddle and shout loudly, demanding that your men look at you. You shout to them that God is with them and that they must continue to fight. You explain that this is a foreign land, and if they were to run then the English would chase them down and kill them like dogs. A cheer erupts. Your words have inspired your men, but they are tired after this morning's fighting.

◊ *If you feel the battle has reached a lull and wish to let your men rest, then go to 89.*

◊ *However, if you feel your men should be able to find the strength for another attack, then go to 18.*

You call Eustace to your side. The proud man meets your gaze with a smile and trots slowly to meet you. As he rides he gestures towards the group of English warriors. He draws up next to you, his back to the enemy. You speak slowly, asking him why he has not yet taken care of these desperate Englishmen.

"William," Eustace replies, "I am pleased to see you. I have just arrived myself. I have not yet ha— " His face twists with pain. He lifts his hands, trying to grasp something from his back. To your horror a stream of blood bubbles from his mouth and nose. Then he slumps forward, revealing an arrow sticking out of his back. It has passed cleanly through his chainmail armour.

You look up and see an English archer amongst the crowd. His comrades are smiling and slapping him on his back, congratulating him on a fine shot. Rage fills your body. You glance down at Eustace. He is still breathing, and you are unsure if the shot will be fatal.

◊ *To teach these English dogs a lesson, go to 86.*
◊ *To get Eustace to safety and leave the English to your men, go to 31.*

Once again the battle is in the balance, and your actions are vital. You race forward, bringing your horse close behind the cavalry who are beginning to falter. This is as close to the enemy as you have been, and you are now in easy range of the English archers. Missiles begin to fall all around you but you ignore the danger. Instead, you shout to the cavalry to turn and fight. You urge them back up the hill towards the enemy.

Slowly your words are heard. Your men do not wish to let you down and they turn to face the enemy once again. Suddenly you are flying through the air and the world goes black.

Colour floods back to your eyes and the noise of battle fills your ears. You find yourself on your back in the mud. Next to you is the bloody body of your horse. An arrow has pierced its skull. You stagger to your feet. You are still halfway up the slope and have no choice but to walk down.

As you return to the centre of the battlefield, a servant appears leading a fresh horse. You lift yourself onto the mount, before looking back to the battle.

The cavalry seem to be working in small groups under the direction of a more experienced knight. They are charging up to the wall, throwing their lances into the English warriors before retreating from the danger of the English spear points. Some cavalry are surging forward in twos and threes, thrusting their lances in the faces of the enemy, and then retreating before they can be killed. The fight goes on for some time, but the English are brave and the shield wall refuses to be broken. It seems the battle has reached a stalemate.

◊ *Go now to 41.*

You turn to your bodyguard, calling a knight to your side and urge him to ride swiftly and bring Odo and Eustace to you.

It is not long before Odo and Eustace are at your side. You explain that they must not let the troops retreat, and that the success at the Battle of Hastings depends on their actions. Your two commanders nod. They race away, Odo to the Normans in the centre and Eustace to the French on the right.

You can do nothing but hope and pray. Your mind turns to the fleeing left wing. Many of the Bretons are still grouped together at the base of the hill. However, they are outnumbered by the English and will soon be slaughtered.

◊ *To risk your life by riding to the aid of the Bretons with your bodyguards, then go to 54.*

◊ *If you feel the role of a commander is to control his army, and feel you have no choice but to leave the Bretons to their fate, do nothing by going to 92.*

26 Despite the eagerness of your cavalry you do not issue the order to charge. Instead, you demand they remain at your side. They are loyal, brave men, and they look shameful that they have misjudged your mood. They return to their position.

Small groups of English are now leaving the battlefield. However, rather than fleeing in panic, they are retreating in a controlled way to the safety of the forest. Eventually you return to your tent, leaving only dead and wounded English remaining on the hill. You are proud of the day's fighting and your victory at the Battle of Hastings.

◊ *Congratulations! You have defeated the English. However, your victory is not complete. Go to 71 to discover your fate.*

You order the small man to be removed from your sight. He struggles as two of your knights drag him away. At last you can concentrate on the battle.

The fight rages on across the hill top. The English shield wall has remained intact, despite your infantry and cavalry bravely throwing themselves against the sturdy shields. It is growing late in the afternoon and the light will soon disappear. You pass the word for your men to fight harder but it is no use, they have been fighting all day and are exhausted. As the sun begins to set your men start to break off from the battle. It is now too dark to fight, and you know that in the morning the brave English warriors will be gone.

◊ *The Battle of Hastings is over and you have failed to defeat the English. Go to 36 to discover your fate.*

You quickly turn to Odo and order him to prepare the cavalry for another attack. He looks confused, but instead of speaking he spurs his horse into the crowd.

Your half-brother re-appears, but as he draws near he says nothing. His gaze remains firmly on your face and you find it difficult to keep eye contact. You then notice that Odo's bodyguards have gathered around you.

"Brother," says Odo, "the day has been hard

and it seems to be affecting your judgement. Another attack would be suicide. I have already lost too many good knights and dear friends to your misguided orders. I can only ask that you retire quietly to your tent, whilst I continue with this fight."

As he stops speaking, six large knights ride forward. The anger in their faces is clear. Your men have lost confidence in your command. You have little choice but to follow the knights from the battlefield.

◊ *The Battle of Hastings is over and you have failed to defeat the English. Go to 36 to discover your fate.*

---

29 It is hopeless! All this death, it's too much for you. You must retreat. Retreat! You ride alongside Odo and begin to explain that too many men are dying, but he interrupts you.

"Brother, I know your feelings are tender, but your men are dying and this is no place for a soft heart." Without another word he surges forward towards the English.

Odo is like a demon unleashed from hell as he races up the slope. He seems unconcerned by the danger of the falling missiles. As he rides he removes his helmet, revealing his face to the Norman warriors who are all about him. Drawing his horse to a stop, he raises his body in his saddle and screams. He urges his men forward, blaring, shouting and even hitting them.

The Norman infantry spring forward with renewed energy. They surge up the hill and slam into the English shield wall. The sight of the Norman infantry inspires you and the rest of your army, and soon all across the battlefield you can see men rise up and push forward. Within minutes the whole of your infantry are fighting hard against the English shield wall.

Your men thrust their swords and spears above and between the shields. However, as time passes it becomes clear the wall is standing firm. This is your last chance to prove your leadership.

◊ *If you feel now is the correct time to order your cavalry to attack, then go to 72.*

◊ *However, if you feel the attack has failed, then you can order your infantry to retreat by going to 35.*

30 The man strides close to your horse and waits. Finally you give him permission to speak.

"Sire," he says. "We have arrows!" At first you are confused, but then you remember that morning you had feared Harold would attack whilst you were unprepared. You had ordered your army to march swiftly. The archers had taken only the arrows they could carry, the rest were left in carts – and now they have arrived.

◊ *Go to 14.*

---

31 The wounding of Eustace boils your blood. You grab Eustace to prevent him falling from his horse. His blood spills onto your clothes. You turn to your men and command them to take Eustace back to camp. Together you begin the long ride back to your tent. As you emerge from the forest you are greeted with a horrific sight. The sun is low in the sky over the battlefield covered with the dead and dying.

You ride slowly to a pile of English bodies. Men gather around you as you look down at the site of Harold's death. You order your men to find his body. After all, he was a noble and deserves a king's burial.

You return slowly to your tent. The day has been hard, yet though your heart is heavy with grief, you know that you are one step closer to being the King of England.

◊ *Congratulations! You have defeated the English. However, your victory is not complete go to 71 to discover your fate.*

The little man is just too annoying and you order your guards to remove him.

The battle on the hill top is slow. Your infantry and cavalry are trying their hardest to disrupt the English shield wall, but it stands firm.

Eventually the sun begins to set and your men move away from the fight and back down the slope. In the gloom you can already see the English starting to slip away. However, it is too dark to order another attack and you know that when the sun rises in the morning the English will be long gone. They will live to fight another day.

◊ *The Battle of Hastings is over and you have failed to defeat the English. Go to 36 to discover your fate.*

33 It takes just a couple of minutes for you and your
bodyguard of about fifty knights to reach the
desperate Bretons. The battle rages in front of you.
The English and your Bretons are intermingled,
spear blades flashing in the sunlight. You draw
your sword and plunge into the action.

Your horse is at full speed as you enter the
scrap and the first Englishmen you meet is simply
knocked aside by your horse as you gallop by. The
second stands no chance as you lean low to your
right, swinging your sword and slicing into his
body as you flash past.

The English seemed shocked. You and your
bodyguard have pushed into the middle of the
fight and the Englishmen are now starting to back
away. They find it hard to fight against the knights,
who are not only more skilful in battle, but also
have the advantage of being high on their horses.

Sensing the fight is lost the English start to head
back up the slope to the safety of the hill top. You
have only been fighting for a few minutes, but the
Bretons now have the upper hand and you decide
to return to the centre. You pass the order to your
knights to finish this fight and then spurring your
horse you start to move away.

◊ *Go to 93.*

34 You are about to spring into the saddle, when an English warrior strides towards you, his weathered face criss-crossed with scars. In his hand he carries a longsword. He stares intently into your eyes and then, to your surprise, a huge grin appears on his face. His teeth are black and rotten. The fight begins.

He moves in a blur – before you can react his sword is high and arching towards your head. It is only the years of training that save you as you drop and roll to your right. His sword thuds into the soil. You rise quickly, slamming your boot into his ribs. However, before you can raise your sword to strike, the old warrior spins around thrusting his shoulder into your chest. You stagger backwards.

The Englishman reacts quickly, bringing his sword up high again and down towards your face. You block and your swords clash together. You do not see his second thrust. The Englishman's sharp blade slices through the rings of your armour and splits your ribs.

You are surprised that you feel no pain. All you can see is the man's face as he pushes closer to you. You can smell his sweat as you gasp your last breaths. With a sudden burst of energy he pushes his sword deeper into your body, its blade slicing into your lungs.

◊ *For you the Battle of Hastings is over. Go to 11 to discover your fate.*

35

As you look out across the battlefield, all you can see are the bodies of your men. You really want to be King of England, but you are not sure that you can live with the deaths of so many people.

You make a decision. You explain to Odo that the fight is hopeless. However, he does not react as you thought. He looks angry and rides away. Odo returns with Eustace of Boulogne, Alan Fergant and about 10 knights. Eustace speaks.

"William, it is time for you to leave us. This battle can be won, but you do not seem to have the courage for the job. I will lead this battle." You are pushed across the battlefield to your tent.

◊ *For you the Battle of Hastings is over. Go to 55 to discover your fate.*

---

36 Rating: OK General

You are not a poor general – but let's be honest, you're not a great general either! You have done well to get this far, but you failed to show the right amount of courage and decisiveness when it counted. You made some poor choices early on in the battle and these came back to haunt you as the fighting progressed. If you can learn from these mistakes, then you will have the potential to be a great general.

◊ *Go now to 1 and prove you have what it takes to win the Battle of Hastings and become King of England…*

You wait and see if the English line is ready to collapse. The men who advanced have been slaughtered on the slope and for a brief second left a gap in the line. However, King Harold sweeps down behind his troops, throwing himself into the gap. For a few seconds he fights alone in the line, his sword swinging in the air. You cannot help but be amazed by his skill. You are sure that in days to come songs and sagas will be created to remember this battle.

Then, as quickly as the hole formed, it is filled by English warriors. They join shields and with the line solid once again, Harold retreats to safety.

The moment has passed.

You sit in silence considering your next move, when a commotion in the crowd of soldiers to your right grabs your attention. You see a short, bearded man walking towards you.

"Sire," he says, "I have come with arrows." At first you are confused, but then you remember. Earlier that day you had ordered the slow-moving carts full of arrows to follow your army. They had many miles to travel and have only now caught up with you.

◊ *If you wish to order the small man to give out the arrows, go to 19.*

◊ *However, if you do not trust him, then go to 44.*

Your half-brother is correct, the time is right for the cavalry to be unleashed. You give Odo permission to attack. He seems pleased and quickly races away to instruct the knights. You watch the battle that is raging on the top of the slope. You guess that hundreds of English have already been killed and looking along their line, you suspect it is shorter then is was this morning. However, the shield wall remains intact and Harold remains alive to guide the battle.

Across the slope your knights race up the hill towards the English. The Normans, French and Bretons have all attacked at the same time. The mass of cavalry looks like a dark brown wave washing up the slope. Then it crashes against the shield wall. The top of the slope becomes choked with warriors. However, the English remain secure behind their shields and your horsemen are forced to ride slowly along the line looking for gaps to attack. When these appear they jump forward, thrusting with their swords or spears into the faces and bodies of the enemy.

Once again the battle has reached a stalemate. You feel a wave of despair. No matter what you try, the English line remains unbroken. As you think about the next move, a strange-looking man appears from the crowd. He is small – about the size of a child – but he has a long flowing beard.

On his back is a bow and in his hands he grasps a bundle of arrows. He stands silently, staring at you, waiting for your permission to speak.

◊ *If you wish to give the strange man a chance to talk, then go to 51.*

◊ *If you are not interested in what the man has to say, go to 67.*

The battle has proven to be more difficult than you imagined. You realise that you must order the infantry to attack again.

The English remain on the lip of the slope and at the first signs of your troops moving, they quickly pack away their kettles and bowls, and form into the shield wall. The slope in front of them is littered with hundreds of dead and dying men and horses. This will make it more difficult to climb. You watch with pride as your men move in a huge wave up the hill. The English begin to hurl missiles into their ranks, but there are not as many as there were this morning. As your men get closer to the enemy shield wall, the advance gathers speed until they are sprinting forward, swords raised high. A huge war cry echoes across the valley. A thunderous crash erupts as the two masses of men meet and fighting breaks out all across the hillside.

The battle soon dissolves into individual scraps, with the English desperately protecting themselves with their shields and your men trying with all their might to smash the wall. Yet, once again, the shields hold.

Odo trots his horse towards you. You greet him warmly and he suggests that the time is right for a cavalry attack.

◊ *If you agree with Odo, then issue the order at 38.*
◊ *If you wish to wait to see what happens, go to 59.*

After hours of fighting, events have finally turned in your favour. As you watch, you see that more and more English warriors are turning to run from the battlefield. The death of their king is just too much. Your infantry continue to fight, pushing hard and breaking holes in the shield wall. All around you your own bodyguard of knights are restless. Mounted on huge warhorses they are moving ahead of you, barely able to stop themselves from charging.

◊ *To unleash your bodyguard, go to 87.*
◊ *If you want your bodyguard to protect you from attack, go to 26.*

The battle continues. Infantry and cavalry clash at the top of the hill. Your warriors try to force back the English shield wall, but it holds its ground. The Normans in the centre are holding out well, and on the right the French warriors are doing slightly better. However, as you examine the battle you notice a problem on the left side of the hill. The Breton warriors, commanded by Fergant, have retreated slightly from the English line and a small gap has appeared between them. Now emerging from the English line is a mass of housecarls – wielding huge axes. They are pushing past their men into the gap between the two armies.

The fearsome housecarls spring into action,

swirling their mighty blades about their bodies as they charge forward. The axes swish through the air, smashing into your men. When the blades hit, they immediately cleave huge holes in the flesh of their victims. Arms and heads are chopped clean from bodies. You even see one axe completely slice through a horse and rider, splitting their bodies in two. Your Breton warriors begin to panic. At first just a few of them turn and run, but the fear spreads like a fire. Within minutes the whole of the Breton force is running back down the hill.

Groups of enemy warriors break away from the English shield wall and charge down after them. The housecarl axe men have remained on the top of the slope.

Panic rises in your stomach but you are given some hope by Alan Fergant. He has managed to collect some of the fleeing warriors under his flag at the base of the slope. They are now grouping together, hoping to make a stand. As the Bretons try to fight for their lives, they trip and stumble in the undergrowth and some even spill into the nearby streams that criss-cross the ground.

The battle is slipping away. The Bretons' retreat has been seen by the rest of your army. To your horror you realise that men on other parts of the battlefield are beginning to edge back from the fight. You now have two problems; the retreat on

the left and the unsteady army in the centre and
right. You must decide which problem you will
deal with first.

◊ *If you wish to send your half-brother Odo and*
  Eustace to stop the retreat in the centre and right,
  then go to 25.
◊ *If you trust your commanders and want to wait and*
  see what happens, then go to 13.

42 You are sick of the killing. You order your men to head back through the forest, trotting quickly past the dead bodies that are strewn across the forest paths. In some places the blood is so thick that it flows like a small stream.

As you emerge from the trees the scene that faces you is one of horror. The battlefield is scattered with the bodies of the dead and dying. Occasional screams of pain pierce the air. In some places, groups of your men have gathered together, starting fires and preparing food in small pots. In other parts, peasants swarm all over the hill top, searching the dead bodies for valuable items, or clothes and weapons they can steal.

You return slowly to your tent. The day has been hard, yet you know you are one step closer to being the King of England.

◊ *Congratulations! You have defeated the English. However, your victory is not complete. Go to 71 to discover your fate.*

---

43 As you watch your cavalry dying under a hail of missiles, you suddenly feel it is impossible to win and that the cavalry must retreat. You turn to your bodyguard and send word to your half-brother Odo to issue the order to retreat. It is not long before you see Odo riding proudly towards your position. However, he does not come to you and instead heads up the slope to the retreating knights. From a distance you can see that he is halting the retreat and instead sending the horsemen back up the slope. For a moment it seems his actions are in vain, then the knights turn back to face the English.

Once again they spring forward, thundering up the slope. The charge is frantic, but as the slope steepens, the charge slows once again. When the knights edge closer to the English line, a mass of missiles begin to arc over the ranks of English into the charging horses. The knights pause and then turn away again from the shield wall. Even Odo's words are not enough.

◊ *If you wish to prove your worth as a commander and urge your men to attack, rush into the battle by moving quickly to 24.*

◊ *However, if you feel the fight is lost, order a full retreat at 35.*

You suspect the strange man may well be a spy and order him out of your sight.

Your focus returns to the battle. All across the hill top you can see your men intermingled with the English as they try desperately to break the shield wall. Your infantry and cavalry fight bravely. Yet as you watch you realise that the chances of you winning the battle are slipping away. It is growing late in the afternoon and the light will soon disappear. You have tried your hardest to break the shield wall and it has been in vain.

At last, as the sun begins to set, you send the word for your men to retreat from the top of the hill. You know that as night comes the enemy will probably slip away from the battlefield but in the darkness you cannot carry on the fight.

◊ *The Battle of Hastings is over and you have failed to defeat the English. Go to 36 to discover your fate.*

Drawing your sword you instruct your knights to follow you as you head across the hill top towards the woods. You are accompanied by about fifty knights, and as you ride you quickly come across English warriors running from the battlefield. These men make easy targets. Mostly the English are running away, and it is a simple task to skewer or slash them down as you ride past.

You are soon in the forest. The ancient trees are large and the undergrowth is thick with leaves that have fallen with the chill of the autumn months. As you enter you are forced to slow down your horse to avoid low hanging branches. Occasionally, you come across English warriors trying to escape. These poor men stand little chance. Most do not even turn to protect themselves.

Suddenly you emerge from the trees into a glade, about twenty paces across. Your eyes take a moment to adjust to the light after the gloom of the forest. It is getting late and the sun is low in the sky, barely visible over the tree tops. You glance about and see that most of your knights have joined you.

◊ *If you wish to continue the pursuit, then go to 91. However, if you have had enough of killing, then declare victory at 5.*

46 You give the order to attack. The knights surrounding you spring into action. However, at the last moment you are unwilling to let events pass you by, and decide to move nearer to the fighting.

As the first cavalrymen reach the line, the English warriors rush forward to try to stop the flood of horses, but the weight of the charge is too much and the weakened wall staggers backwards and begins to collapse. Knights force their way between the shields and pour into the space behind.

You spur your horse on, pushing into the line, knocking English and Norman warriors aside in your haste. One, then two English fyrds spring into your path, but you kill them easily as your blade swings about your horse. You push onwards, breaking through the enemy line into the space behind.

◊ *Go to 78.*

47 Your knights are upon the bodyguards in an instant. As the first knights slam into the housecarls some English warriors are thrown high in the air. Within minutes the housecarls are slaughtered.

Ahead of you, few English warriors survive. The only ones left fighting are the housecarls in the centre, yet even as you watch they begin to retreat from the battlefield. They now join the hundreds of Englishmen who race to the forest.

You know the fight is over, but you wonder if the battle is won. Though you have managed to capture the hill and defeat the English army, many enemy warriors remain alive. If too many English warriors are allowed to escape they will simply group together and fight another day.

◊ *If you wish to claim victory now, then go to 99.*

◊ *If you wish to chase down the remaining English warriors, then continue at 45.*

You pass the order for the infantry to attack. Your men hesistate, but soon push forward. You watch with pride as your infantry advance slowly, to avoid slipping on the blood-red grass. When they are about halfway up the slope, the missiles begin to rain down from behind the English line.

The advance slows. Some men crouch low to the ground, others lift their shields to cover their backs. For a moment it looks as if the missiles will beat the infantry back once again. At that moment a huge Norman warrior suddenly springs forward. He lifts his hands into the air, bellows the Norman war cry "Thor's aid", and rushes forward at the English. For a moment he is alone, sprinting to his death. Then, from across the battlefield the war cry begins to echo until it is a wall of sound. All across the slope warriors spring forward.

Your men smash into the English shield wall with force. At first the wall is pushed back and the English fight hard to recover. However, the battle soon dissolves into individual fights, with the English protected by their shields and your men desperately trying to slash and smash at the wall, and the men behind. Once again the shields hold and the fight grinds into stalemate. The only option left is for a feint attack. You reluctantly pass the word for the cavalry to charge forward.

◊ *Go to 8.*

49 As you look into your half-brother's eyes you feel rage burning inside your stomach. Before you can control yourself you scream in anger. You insist he follows your orders to attack – now! Despite your rage he just sits in silence. Without thinking you strike your half-brother's cheek.

Odo is shocked by the blow, but doesn't react. Instead he lifts his hand to his mouth, touching his bloody lip. He shakes his head. His refusal to react is too much for you. Suddenly the world goes red as anger engulfs you. Your hand moves to your sword, grasping the hilt.

This time your half-brother reacts quickly. He leans forward and grasps your sword arm. His face is now close to yours.

"William, the battle is over for you. If you draw your sword I will be forced to kill you." Odo's words shock you and you feel the anger subsiding. He turns to his men who have gathered close by. "Our general is not feeling too well. Escort him to his tent. I will command the army."

◊ *For you the Battle of Hastings is over. Go to 11 to discover your fate.*

---

50 You watch on as the fight continues to rage at the top of the slope. At first it seems that the feint attack may have disrupted the wall. In parts it has buckled and folded in on itself. Your men are

fighting hard to force their way into these areas.
However, King Harold is aware of the danger and
he quickly directs men from other parts of the
battle to fill the gaps. The English line has held
firm. You feel you have no choice but to order
another feint attack.

◊   *Go to 64.*

You signal for the strange little man to speak.

"Sire," he says, bowing as he speaks, "I bring
great news. My men have been toiling all day to
bring our carts to the battlefield. Now we are here.
The battle is saved."

You look on in astonishment at this little man.

"Sire, what should I do with my arrows? I have
thousands."

Suddenly you remember. When you advanced
this morning you were forced to leave behind
the slow moving carts that carried the supply of
arrows. You had ordered the archers to bring only
the arrows they could carry. However, these were
shot in the opening stages of the battle. You had
instructed the archers to leave the battlefield and
had forgotten all about them, until now.

◊   *If you wish to order the man to give out the arrows,*
    go to 98.
◊   *If you think he may be mad, go to 44.*

As the order is passed to the archers to shoot their new arrows into the mass of fighting men at the top of the slope, some begin to turn in your direction with a look of confusion and disbelief in their eyes. However, it is not long before the archers prepare for the first volley.

Slowly the archers draw their bows. They lift the point of the arrow, aiming high into the sky. The sun is low and in the eyes of the English troops. You can see that many of those not engaged in battle have lifted their hands to shield their eyes from the sun's glare.

Suddenly the strings snap back and the arrows fly into the air. The black cloud rises into the sky, before falling on the heads of the troops fighting on the ridge. The archers quickly shoot again.

You soon realise your mistake. The arrows are falling into the crowd of men fighting on the slope. You watch with horror as they rain down on the mass of men, piercing bodies and puncturing helmets. It is not just English warriors that are hit, many of your men are intermingled with the enemy and they too are being killed and wounded.

◊ *If you wish to let you archers continue the onslaught, then go to 76.*

◊ *However, if you wish to order your men to shoot into the English ranks behind where your troops are fighting, go to 63.*

By your side are hundreds of your knights – some of the best fighters in the world. A single charge from your men will destroy what is left of the English army. Yet, the English are noble warriors and you decide to offer them the chance to give up.

Turning to the nearest knight, you instruct him to ride forward and urge the English to surrender. He rides to within a few paces of the enemy and raises his voice. He urges the housecarls to surrender, promising that they will be unharmed.

The English reply is slow in coming. For a split second you feel they are going to accept the surrender. However, a single arrow flies from the ranks of the enemy, slamming into the chest of your messenger. It punches through his body – the blood-soaked tip clearly visible as it emerges from his back. As the messenger's body topples from his horse, rage fills the air. The sight of the death of the messenger is too much and without an order from you, the knights charge forward.

◊ *Go to 47.*

It takes only a couple of minutes for you and your bodyguard of fifty knights to reach the desperate Bretons. With a yell you draw your mighty broadsword and plunge into the battle. The first Englishman you meet stands no chance as your weapon rips into his back. His armour is useless against your razor sharp blade and a huge wound opens up. The next warrior sees you coming and raises his sword high in the air. However, you are a skilful swordsman and you slash into the man's neck. As you rush past, you see his head bounce on the ground.

The arrival of your knights has turned the small fight at the base of the slope to your favour. Many of the English now begin to head back up the slope to safety. The Bretons now have the upper hand and you decide to return to the centre. You pass the order to your knights to finish this fight.

Your horse has taken only a few strides when a spear hits. You actually see the weapon leaving the hands of a tall warrior only seconds before it slams into your horse's flank. You twist round as the beast falls, slipping from the saddle and landing on your feet. You are furious and rush through the crowd. Your sword is out. You ignore all about you, focusing on the man who killed your horse. He feigns a slice to your legs but instead aims a blow to your face. However he is an unskilled warrior, a dangerous thing to be when facing a Norman knight. You block his strike with ease. With your left hand you punch him in the face – breaking his nose. The warrior raises his hands. It is his final move. You quickly slice your sword across his exposed stomach, spilling his intestines.

You leave the man to die in the mud.

You glance around for another horse just as Eustace appears from the crowd. Angers flushes your face as you realise he has disobeyed your order to steady his men. He rushes to your side and leaps from his horse and offers you the reins.

"Sire, take my mount, I will find another." You are loath to accept Eustace's offer, but the battle is more important than your pride.

◊ *If you wish to return to the centre to take command of your army then go to 60.*

◊ *If you feel you can do more good here and wish to keep fighting, then go to 34.*

55 Rating: Hopeless General

Let's face it you are not cut out to be a medieval general. You are weak and timid, and give up at the first hurdle. In fact, you should consider a job as a milkmaid! If you are to be successful at the Battle of Hastings you need to be more ruthless, show more courage and listen to the advice your generals are trying to offer.

◊ *Now go back to section 1 and try again…*

56

You give Ivo permission to charge and he spurs his horse into action. Your men roar as Ivo rides between the two armies before thrusting the tip of his lance into the ground. Then he begins to sing! The words drift to your ears and you recognise the song as that of Roland, a knight who died gloriously in battle.

Ivo finishes the song and pulls his sword from its scabbard. He begins to throw it high into the air, letting it twist and turn before catching it safely. Your army gasp and cheer with each throw. However, Ivo's display is too much for the English and suddenly a mounted English knight bursts from the ranks, his long lance lowered. Ivo sheathes his sword and races towards his lance, pulling it cleanly from the ground.

The two knights charge at each other with lances lowered. The English knight's shield is pulled up high to protect his body, but Ivo has no shield. At the last moment Ivo twists his body and the tip of the English lance swishes past harmlessly. At the same time, Ivo's lance smashes into the shield of the English knight. The shield and lance splinter, and the knight is thrown backwards off his horse. Ivo jumps from his mount, his sword drawn before he lands. Ivo strides towards the Englishman, bends down, grabs a fistful of hair and pulls the head up. In a flash, Ivo brings down his sword. Blood spurts freely as Ivo lifts the head high into the air.

Ivo Taillefer begins to turn slowly, gathering speed. After three spins he releases the head. It arches high into the air and bounces twice before coming to a stop just short of the English shield wall. Ivo vaults back onto his horse and begins a charge towards the English line. His horse thunders up the slope, slowing only when the ground gets steeper. Finally, he smashes into the enemy's shield wall. You watch as he is engulfed. The English swords stab and slash at his body. Suddenly he emerges on foot, covered in blood. He staggers to a nearby tree and collapses to the ground. Ivo has died a hero's death and his actions will be remembered forever.

◊ *Now move quickly to 83 to begin the battle…*

What really happened?

No one knows what really happened at the battle of Hastings in 1066! What we do know is that soon after the battle William returned to Normandy leaving Bishop Odo in charge. But Odo was a poor leader and when Eustace of Boulogne was accused of attacking Dover, William was forced to return to England. In the years that followed, many revolts sprung up but each of these was crushed ruthlessly by William.

People will try to convince you that they know what happened at the Battle of Hastings. The truth is that the real events have been lost in the mists of time, and we have no reliable accounts written by people who were actually at the battle. What we do have are poems and books written many years after the battle, and a big woven picture called the Bayeux tapestry.

So here's the best guess of what happened at the Battle of Hastings:

- ◊ Harold forced William to fight by positioning his army between Pevensey and London.
- ◊ Harold had no cavalry and fought on top of Senlac Hill using the shield wall tactic.
- ◊ William started the battle with a hail of arrows.
- ◊ The battle lasted all day.
- ◊ At some point infantry and cavalry both attacked the shield wall, but it held firm.

◊ The Bretons on the left ran away and the English followed, but William's army survived.
◊ King Harold was killed, the shield wall collapsed and lots of English were slaughtered.

Here's a list of things that historians think may have happened:
◊ Harold was waiting for William at Senlac Hill and had stuck wooden stakes in the ground at the bottom of the slope.
◊ Ivo Taillefer attacked the English on his own at the start of the battle.
◊ Norman knights carried out three feint attacks.
◊ William had three horses killed from under him during the fighting.
◊ William's army nearly ran away when they thought he was dead. The only way to stop this was for William to remove his helmet and show his men his face.
◊ King Harold was killed by an arrow in the eye or King Harold was hacked to death by Norman knights – your choice.
◊ Battle Abbey at the battlefield was built on the exact spot of Harold's death.

◊ *Did you manage to get a great general rating? If not, go to 1 to try again, and become as great as William the Conqueror.*

58 You are sure your men will recognise you without the risk of removing your helmet. Yet, as you wait proudly, you can feel the panic begin to spread across the battlefield. Voices are beginning to be raised. You even notice that some men have turned and are leaving the battle. Your warriors still think that you are dead!

Eustace once again pushes his horse next to you and leans in close so that his voice can be heard.

"William, you must go to your men and show your face. Prove that you are alive. Act now before this battle is lost and we are beaten by a rumour."

◊ *If you wish to swallow your pride and follow Eustace's advice, then move on to 22 now.*

◊ *If you wish to ignore Eustace then slip to 70 with a prayer on your lips.*

---

59 You instruct Odo that the time is not right. Your attention returns to the battle, watching as it rages on before your eyes. Your warriors continue to fight, pushing hard to smash the wall. They try desperately to break the English line, yet whenever one English warrior is killed another quickly takes his place.

Your thoughts are suddenly broken by a deep voice.

"Brother, why do you sit so?" There is a pause, but you do not respond. Odo continues to speak.

"No matter. Do you wish me to order the cavalry
to attack now?"

◊ *If you wish to let Odo order the cavalry to attack,
   then go to 38.*
◊ *If you wish to ignore Odo and wait to
   see what happens, move on to 73.*

Eustace's horse is an amazing beast. It gracefully
moves along as you return to the mound in
the centre of your army. The enemy on the left
are returning to the slope, and the Bretons are
reforming. You are relieved to see that Odo and
Eustace have done their job well, and your army
has stopped retreating from the enemy. However,
you see that your men are no longer acting as
one mass of warriors. Instead, they are fighting in
small groups, many glancing over their shoulders
in your direction.

Something is wrong. Eustace bursts from the
crowd on a brown horse. He speaks quickly.

"A rumour has spread that you have died
fighting with the Bretons. The men are threatening
to run from the field."

◊ *If you wish to prove to your men that you are still
   alive by riding amongst them, then go to 22.*
◊ *If you wish to wait a moment and see what happens
   next, then go to 58.*

61 Odo and Eustace sit quietly on their horses waiting for your response. Odo is right when he says your men are tired, but you are keen to keep up the fight. You gather your strength and turn to Odo, insisting that he orders the attack. He looks directly into your eyes and says softly, "Brother, it will be suicide. Our men must rest."

◊ *If you wish to insist that Odo issues the order to attack, go to 49.*

◊ *If you feel rest is perhaps the best option, then go to 89.*

---

62 You watch on in silence as the battle rages. There is an ebb and flow, much like water on the seashore. Sometimes your men gain the upper hand and the shield wall moves backwards. Yet, when this happens, King Harold is always there, rushing about behind his men directing reserves and even jumping into battle himself. This goes on and on. English warriors die, your men die and yet the English still hold the line.

Suddenly you see a familiar face, as your half-brother Odo emerges from the crowd.

"Brother, why do you not order the cavalry to try a feint attack?" ask Odo.

◊ *To do as Odo suggests, order the charge at 8.*

◊ *If you wish to wait and see what happens, then go to 37.*

You pass the order for your archers to shoot over the heads of your men and into the English ranks behind. Suddenly, the archers release the strings and a whoosh fills the air as the cloud of arrows rises up before plunging down onto the heads of the men behind the line of fighting warriors. The archers shoot again and again and again.

You now search the devastation for King Harold. He is easy to spot, standing firm behind his men, shouting commands, sword in hand. As you watch he is engulfed by a cloud of arrows. The shafts thud into the ground all around him and he suddenly looks scared. For some reason he stares up into the sky, as if to see if the arrows have come from God. It is at that moment that he is hit. An arrow curves down and strikes the King on the front of his helmet. You gasp as the King's hand springs to his face, grasping the shaft of the arrow that now extends from his helmet. The English warriors that are close to the King suddenly stop fighting and instead swing to look at their leader. They look scared. The shield wall in front of Harold's position begins to buckle as your Norman warriors sense the change in the battle.

◊ *The moment has arrived – victory is in the air!*
  Go swiftly to 66.

You quickly move your horse and find Odo. You tell him to try another feint attack. If more English fyrds can be killed, then perhaps the shield wall will weaken. Then he hurries away to organise the knights.

As you move back to the centre of the battle, you can see Ralf of Tosny lead the second charge. The attack is further along the line than the first.

Suddenly Ralf of Tosny breaks away from the wall. His men follow him once again.

You wait. Will the English follow?

Nothing…

Then, the English emerge from the line. They break from the protection of the wall, screaming and shouting. This time hundreds of fyrds flow after the knights. The knights wait until the English are at the base of the slope. Then they turn, swords drawn.

The fight is quick and bloody. The second feint has been a success!

◊ *If you wish to try the feint attack for a third time, then issue the order at 100.*

◊ *If you feel the English will not fall for the trick a third time, go to 37.*

65 The archers don't stop to enjoy their deadly work, and instead continue to shoot. They are so fast that you are sure that the first arrows are still in the air when the second are being released.

The enemy try to avoid the arrows, but at this range thin armour and flimsy shields are of little use. You see many brave English warriors crouching beneath their shields, only to be skewered as the arrows splinter the wood.

You search the devastation for King Harold. He is easy to find standing proudly, like a beacon, in the centre of his army. At first he seems unaware of the arrows and continues to direct his men as the shafts hammer into the ground around him. Yet as the number of arrows increases, he seems to become more concerned. You watch as he looks into the sky, lifting his hand to shield his eyes from the sun. Suddenly, an arrow slams into his helmet and into the King's face. He drops to his knees, his hands grasping the bloody shaft.

The English warriors closest to the King suddenly stop fighting – swinging around to look at their leader. The shield wall in front of Harold's position begins to buckle.

The moment has arrived.

◊ *To order your knights to attack, go to 85.*

◊ *To lead the charge yourself, go to 81.*

66 It quickly becomes clear that the King is seriously wounded, although he is not dead. You can see him slumped behind the line of English warriors, propped up by his loyal housecarls, who now surround him. An arrow shaft extends from his helmet, but he is moving.

The injury to Harold has caused chaos in the English line. Just in front of where he has fallen, the shield wall has been pushed back by your men. It is starting to buckle and gaps have appeared in the line. In some places housecarl axe men have rushed to fill the gaps, their mighty blades swirling in the air keeping your Norman warriors back. The English are fighting hard to keep the wall in place, but you can sense that it is on the verge of collapse. One final attack may be all that is needed.

◊ *To send your knights forward, go to 46.*

◊ *To lead your knights in the attack yourself, go to 12.*

You glance at the peasant. His dirty face and
ragged clothes do not mark him out as a
warrior. But he stares intently at your face, and
whenever you glance in his direction his blue eyes
immediately make contact, forcing you to look
away quickly. You try to ignore him, but he is eager
to speak.

◊ *If you wish to hear what the strange man has to say,*
go to 51.

◊ *However, if you wish to ignore him, then go silently*
to 32.

Confusion surrounds you. Your Norman infantry
are just standing, looking across the hill top to
the housecarl warriors. You turn to your men and
tell them that though they have fought hard all
day they must now give one final sacrifice. You
explain that God is with them and they must
charge forward and sweep the English from the
battlefield. Your words are met by a huge cheer,
and the Norman infantry surge forward to attack.
You now turn to a nearby knight. You tell him to
find the other commanders and instruct them to
bring all their men to the battle on the hill top.

Suddenly, an English housecarl axeman appears
on your right, about five paces from your horse.
Without thinking your hand drops to your side
and you draw your sword. You pull on the reins,

instinctively moving the horse to protect your body. The housecarl leaps forward and crashes into the flank of your horse. The blow sends you flying, and you roll backwards off your horse.

For a moment you are in the air, but as you hit the ground you spring to your feet. You have your sword, but your helmet has come off and rolled away.

The housecarl is upon you. His huge frame fills your vision and he has lifted his axe above his head. As you watch, the blade cuts through the air, arcing down. You duck to the left, letting the axe blade fly harmlessly into the ground. In that split second the housecarl is unbalanced and you bring your sword up, aiming directly for his stomach. However, the old fighter is fast. He brings the handle of his axe up to block your sword, then rolls his shoulder into your chest. You stagger backwards.

Regaining your balance, you swing your sword at the man's head. He is ready and ducks under the blow with amazing skill. The weight of your sword carries your arm across his body. You are unbalanced. The warrior springs into the air and swings his axe down again. You are seconds away from death.

◊ *To duck, go to 2.*
◊ *To block the blow, go to 84.*

It is clear that the English army is beaten. Small groups of English warriors have joined together in groups and continue to fight, but they are outnumbered by your men.

The only group of men left unharmed are the group of housecarls that surround the fallen figure of the English King. His armour is now red with blood and he is completely still. The shaft of the arrow is still lodged in his face.

◊ *If you wish to make sure the King is dead, then go to 97.*

◊ *If you wish to let the English army retreat with pride, then claim your victory at 82.*

70 Despite Eustace's pleas you still feel that your men will recognise you without removing your helmet. It is a great mistake. As time has passed and they have not been able to see you, the rumour has grown. Your men now look around, trying to catch a glimpse of you, but in the heat of battle knights look very similar.

At first you can see only a few men making their way from the battlefield, but the numbers increase. The fight continues on the hill and the battle rages on, but slowly your men are drifting away. Then the panic begins to spread. You watch as hundreds of your men start dropping their weapons and running from the fight.

As men begin to stream past your position you remove your helmet. You ride amongst your men, showing your face and screaming for them to stop. But it is no good.

Suddenly, a loud hoot rises from the English horns and the English infantry spring forward in pursuit of your men. All you can do now is hope that you can escape.

◊ *For you the Battle of Hastings is over. Go to 11 to discover your fate.*

---

71 Rating: Good General

Well done! You have proved yourself to be a good medieval general. You understand when to take risks, and the best way to use you troops when it counts. You also know when to take advice from your commanders, and when to ignore it. In 1066, the real William the Conqueror was more ruthless than you have been and he chased all the English from the battlefield. He knew that if he could destroy the English army then they would be unable to rise again to fight another day.

You now have two choices.

◊ *You can either go back to 1 and fight the battle again to prove you are in fact a great general after all, or you can go to 57 to discover what really happened at the Battle of Hastings…*

In total you have almost 2,000 mounted warriors on the battlefield. Soon the cavalry have moved to the bottom of the slope and are ready to attack. Once again the French are positioned on the right, the Normans in the centre and the Bretons over on the left.

The horses and riders spring forward and stream up the slope in a deadly wave to sections of the English shield wall that your infantry have not fought.

The cavalry gallop up the cluttered slope and have to slow down to avoid the dead and dying bodies. This is the moment Harold has been waiting for. A dark cloud of missiles flies over the ranks of the fighting infantry. Arrows, javelins, slingshots, small axes and stones smash into the horses and riders. Metal points, sharp blades and heavy stones easily rip through horse flesh, causing many to stumble and fall.

The onslaught is too much and like the infantry before them, the charge slows and halts. As you watch you see the riders pulling their horses away from the fight and turning to move back down the slope. Your cavalry are retreating and you must act now! This may be the time for you to get involved.

◊ *To risk your life and race forward to stop the cavalry from retreating, go to 24.*

◊ *If you feel the missiles are too much for your cavalry, then issue the order for them all to retreat by going to 15.*

You slowly begin to realise that the English are too strong for your attacks. Their shield wall is holding strong and as their men die, more of their warriors step in to protect the line.

The sun is hanging low in the sky. There are only a few hours of daylight left. Odo was right when he suggested that you should use your cavalry to attack the English and now you have missed the chance.

Eventually the night comes and the sun finally sinks from the sky. The battle is over, and you order your men to retreat from the hill. They set up camp for the night. You know that when they awake the English will be gone.

◊ *The Battle of Hastings is over and you have failed to defeat the English. Go to 36 to discover your fate.*

The hours of fighting on the top of the slope has seen your warriors become tangled amongst the English. In some places it is impossible to tell which men are yours and which are the enemy. You realise that if the archers shoot high into the air, the arrows will arch over the mix of men and into the English behind.

You watch carefully as the line of archers steps forward and aims high into the blue autumn sky. The archers release the strings and a whoosh fills the air as the cloud of arrows rises up before plunging down onto the heads of the men behind the line of fighting warriors. Then they quickly shoot again and again and again.

You search the English line for King Harold. He is easy to spot, standing firm behind his men, shouting commands, sword in hand. As you watch he is engulfed by a cloud of arrows. An arrow curves down and strikes the King on the front of his helmet. You gasp as the King's hand springs to his face. The English warriors that are close by stop fighting. They look scared. The shield wall in front of Harold's position begins to buckle as your Norman warriors sense the change in the battle.

◊ *The moment has arrived – victory is in the air!*
Go swiftly to 66.

---

75 Your men are still willing to fight and the retreat was a mistake. The infantry have collected at the base of the hill. They are huddled together in desperate groups. You decide that you must speak to your men. You spur your horse forward, lifting your helmet at the same time. With your face exposed you address the warriors. You tell them that it was a mistake to order the brave warriors to retreat in the face of the cowardly English. You tell them to go back to their positions and prepare to attack once again.

Your men seem reluctant to move, but slowly

they prepare for the attack. Your heart is filled with pride as the wave of heavily armoured men push quickly up the slope. However, the advance up the hill falters as missiles rain down once more. Your warriors crouch bravely under their shields, unable to move forward. You must react now!

◊ *To ride forward and urge your infantry to continue the attack, go to 16.*

◊ *If you would rather retreat again and save the lives of your men by ordering the retreat, go to 29.*

English warriors fall with your own men under a hail of arrows, with very little effect on the shield wall. Harold has organised his men so that as one part of the wall weakens, fresh troops move in to plug the gap.

Eventually the rain of death stops as your archers run out of arrows. Yet the fight continues on the slope. The English look as strong as ever and your disastrous decision to kill your own men has worked in their favour. You have weakened your own attack and you suddenly realise you will not break the wall today.

The battle continues to rage, but as the sun falls low in the sky it is clear you must order the retreat.

◊ *The Battle of Hastings is over and you have failed to defeat the English. Go to 36 to discover your fate.*

The fight at the trench is over. It is becoming dark and the battle must end. You spur your horse back through the trees, and along the path that you rode down only minutes earlier. Your sword feels heavy in your hand and your muscles scream in pain. You are exhausted; even the simple act of returning your sword to its sheath seems beyond you at this point. You are bruised and cut from when you were thrown from your horse and hit by English blades. You have lost your helmet, broken your lance and in places your fine armour is torn and slashed.

You emerge back onto the battlefield to be greeted by a sight from hell. The sun is now beginning to set and hangs low in the sky. Yet, the weak light still illuminates the hill top, showing the terrible carnage of battle. Bodies are scattered everywhere, though in some places, where the fighting was at its fiercest, they are stacked three or four high. Some of these bodies are intact and appear simply to be sleeping, whilst others are clearly dead. Arms, legs and even heads have been clearly severed and many bodies have huge gashes and cuts that leak so much blood that the soil surrounding them is a deep red.

As you ride you come across a pile of bodies larger than any other. It is located almost exactly in the centre of the hill top. Your memory of the

day's events is already fading, but it must be the site of Harold's last stand. You ride slowly to the pile and stop, gazing down at the dead bodies. A small group of your men quickly gather around. You order them to guard the site from looters. You also instruct them to uncover the body of the King, telling them it is at the bottom of the gruesome pile. You remind them that he is a king and deserves a king's burial.

You leave your men to their dreadful job and return to your tent. The day has been hard, but you know you are one step closer to sitting in your rightful place as King of England.

◊ *Congratulations! You have defeated the English. Victory is complete. Your name will live in history as a great general. Go to 88 to discover why.*

---

78 You emerge on the other side of the English fighting line. In front of you is open ground, where most of the arrows fell during the second onslaught. Hundreds of shafts stick out of the ground. The grass is also covered by many English bodies.

Quickly, you look around for your knights. You are surprised when Eustace and his knights appear. You catch his eyes and he smiles and then raises his arm, pointing to your left. You swing your head to see that he is pointing at the defenceless King of England.

Harold is slumped on the ground. He is still alive, the arrow you had seen earlier buried in his helmet. His left hand is held to his face, blood seeping through his fingers and pouring down the back of his arm. In his right hand he weakly grips his sword. Though he is surrounded by warriors, they have their backs to you. God is truly on your side.

◊ *To wait and see what happens, go to 69.*

◊ *To race forward and slaughter the King of England, move to 97.*

The hours of fighting on the top of the slope have seen your warriors become tangled amongst the English. However, you realise that if the archers shoot high into the air, the arrows will pass over the mix of men and down onto the English.

The line of archers steps forward and shoots arrows high into the autumn sky. The cloud of arrows rises up before arcing down onto the heads of the men behind the line of fighting warriors. They continue to shoot.

The enemy try to avoid the arrows. Some crouch beneath their shields, but many simply die as the black shafts bury themselves into their bodies. You can feel the English panic in the air. They thought you had no arrows left!

You now search the devastation for King Harold. He is easy to find, standing proudly with his men. Suddenly, he looks scared. He stares up into the sky, as if to see if the arrows have come from God. It is at that moment that he is hit. You gasp as the King's hand springs to his face, grasping the shaft of the arrow that now extends from his helmet. He drops to his knees and disappears from your view. The shield wall in front of Harold's position begins to buckle and move backwards as your Norman warriors sense the change in the battle. The moment has arrived.

◊ *To order your knights to attack, go to 85.*

◊ *To lead the charge yourself, go to 81.*

---

80 The sun is now high in the sky. From your position, high on your horse, you can see the battlefield clearly. The English warriors moved quickly at the first signs that your men were preparing to attack, forming up into the shield wall.

Your infantry gather solemnly at the base of the hill. The slope between your men and the English shield wall is littered with shattered spears and discarded swords. Broken bodies of dead and dying warriors lie in the grass. At the top of the hill, where the fighting has been the fiercest, the bodies of your men and the enemy lie next to each other forming a gruesome barrier.

You pass the order for the attack to begin. Your infantry stride purposefully up the slope. However, almost as soon as the advance begins, missiles fly up from behind the shield wall. You have seen this before and your stomach tightens as the black objects fall from the sky onto your men. This morning the missiles stopped the attack, but now it is different. The advance slows, but your warriors have a new purpose. You see many men crouch lower to the ground – some lift their shields to cover their backs – but they do not stop.

Your army smashes into the English shield wall with force. However, the battle soon dissolves into individual fights, with the English protected by their shields and your men desperately trying to slash and stab at the wall and the men behind.

◊ *If you feel now is the right time to order the first feint attack, go to 8.*

◊ *However, if you feel the time is not yet right, go instead to 62.*

Seeing that the English shield wall is unsteady, you rush forward to attack. You jam your feet into the flanks of your horse and it springs forward. You draw your sword. At the bottom of the slope you glance over your shoulder – you are alone. You surge up the slope without stopping.

At last you reach the English line. Warriors fight in vicious hand-to-hand combat all about you trying to rip flesh, spill blood and smash bone.

You urge your horse forward, aiming for a gap in the wall where two shields have become separated. The first enemy warrior you meet is a man with a shock of red hair. You simply push your horse forward, knocking the man off his feet.

You are now behind the English line and all about you English warriors flood past. Then, from the crowd a huge troll of a man emerges. He is armed with a mighty two-handed axe, though he is so strong he can swing it with just one arm. He has a round shield strapped to his other arm. The man raises his huge axe, aiming at your head. You duck – the blade misses you by inches. However, the axe embeds itself in the neck of your horse. Blood spurts from the wound and the warm liquid sprays on your face. The horse immediately buckles and crashes into the ground.

The wind is knocked from your chest and for a moment you lie stunned on the floor. The huge

Englishman swings his axe down again. You are surprised when it slams into your chest. You look down – your chest is a mass of red blood, punctured flesh and white bone. You know you are dying, yet you feel no pain – only a quiet peace. Your thoughts drift to your home in Normandy, just before you die.

◊ *The Battle of Hastings is over and you have failed to defeat the English. Go to 36 to discover your fate.*

82 The sun is now low in the sky and the battle will soon come to an end. You pass the order to your bodyguard to chase away the remaining English warriors, and turn your horse towards your tent.

As you ride slowly back down the slope, a tear forms in your eye as you see the bodies of your men and the noble English warriors on the slope. Headless bodies, severed arms and unattached legs litter the ground. Blood has seeped into the grass turning it red.

The price you and your men have paid is high, but you have been victorious. All that is now left to do is to claim your rightful place as the King of England.

◊ *Congratulations! You have defeated the English. However, your victory is not complete. Go to 71 to discover your fate.*

83 King Harold stands behind his men with a cluster of flags marking his position. He has formed his 8,000 warriors into a shield wall with his best troops, the housecarls, in the front ranks. Behind these fearsome fighters are the less well armed fyrds. These are mostly farmers, and have little experience of battle. Scattered throughout the English line are small groups of housecarl axe men, wielding axes so large that they need both hands to lift them.

You give the signal to your trumpeter to start the attack. Your archers step forward, then release a mass of arrows into the air, blackening the sky. You watch as wave after wave of arrows hiss through the air and thud down into the English line. Some pierce English bodies, but most land harmlessly.

Your archers are doing little damage, so now you turn to your infantry. Close by is your bodyguard of knights. You turn to one knight and instruct him to find Eustace, Odo and Fergant and give them the order to attack with their infantry. The knight rushes away and it takes a few minutes before you see movement all across the battlefield. Your infantry moves forward and takes position at the base of the hill.

You watch with pride as the heavily armoured men push quickly up the hill. However, the slope is steep and the advance slows. The English seem to have been waiting for this moment and suddenly they throw objects down upon your men. At first it is only stones or small axes, but soon the English are throwing and firing anything they can find. Arrows, javelins and slingshot all arch high into the air before slamming down onto your men.

You watch with growing worry as the advance stops halfway up the slope. The ground is

scattered with dead and dying men. Many others
have dropped to their knees or crouched down,
trying to use their shields to protect themselves
from the deadly missiles.

◊ *To order your men to ignore the missiles and
continue the attack, go to 16.*

◊ *To order your men to retreat from the missiles,
move on to 9.*

84 As the axe cuts through the air, you try to block the blow with your sword. You are not quick enough. The axe slices under your blade and smashes you in the face.

Blackness…

The last thing you remember is the salty taste of your own blood in your mouth. Pain seers through your skull for a second but then disappears. Instead, you feel a calmness spreading across your body as you draw your last breath.

◊ *You have defeated the English. However, your death in glorious battle means your victory is not complete. Go to 71 to discover your fate.*

---

85 For the first time in the battle, the shield wall has moved. Small gaps have appeared as English warriors turn to desperately look for news of their king. The panic spreads quickly. Some English warriors break from the front line and retreat towards their king. Others are already running for the safety of the forest.

Seizing the moment you scream the order for the knights to attack. Your bodyguard hear your words above the din of the battle and spring forward. Hundreds of your cavalry join the charge and they stream up the slope towards the weakened shield wall.

The horses smash into the enemy with a sound

you will never forget. The English warriors
are thrown backwards and up in the air by the
charging horses. At first, only single horses break
through, but soon you can see small groups of
horses behind the front line. That's when you
realise that something is wrong.

Not enough English warriors have retreated
and your attacks all day have not killed enough of
the English. Now, when you have finally made a
breakthrough, it seems that the enemy is still too
strong. English warriors swarm from all over the
battlefield to the place where their wall is broken.
Slowly they regain the advantage. Man by man,
they push forward, joining shields and slowly
reforming the shield wall. You watch in horror as
your men are pushed back to the lip of the slope by
the English shield wall.

The battle continues, though the day is now late
and the sun is hanging low in the sky. Eventually,
the night falls. The battle is over and you order
your men to retreat from the hill.

◊ *The Battle of Hastings is over and you have failed to
defeat the English. Go to 36 to discover your fate.*

Anger wells in the pit of your stomach as the
reality of Eustace's injury hits you. The arrow – the
most cowardly of all weapons – might have killed
him, but in the back too! A red mist engulfs you as

rage takes over your body and you lose control.
Before you realise what is happening, you have
thrown away the broken lance and drawn your
sword. Your horse strides towards the small group
of English warriors. You are alone.

Your horse takes a few steps, then stops – its
head pulling to the right. You see that a knight is
grasping the reins of your horse. You cannot hear
what he is saying and your vision is blurred. Then
slowly you regain control.

You realise that the knight stopped you from
charging alone. You look away, embarrassed by
your lack of control. When you look up again he is
gone! You glance behind you to see your knights
waiting for orders. You wonder if the vanishing
knight was an angel sent from God.

Having regained control, you act quickly.
You issue the order for Eustace to be taken away
for treatment and for the remaining knights to
prepare for an attack. You turn your attention to
the English position. The dip in the ground is wide
and deep, forming a trench in front of the enemy.
You realise that it would be impossible for your
knights to charge across. You tell them to dismount
and attack on foot.

It takes a few minutes for the knights to prepare,
but soon they are ready. The men jog forward.
Then, when they are about fifty paces from the

trench, a huge war cry erupts from your knights and they sprint forward. The first few knights to reach the trench leap high into the air, clearing the obstacle and landing awkwardly in the undergrowth. But they are cut down as the English swarm over them. The rest of your men clamber quickly across the trench and into the fight. The English stand little chance. However, they fight well and many of your knights are cut down by the housecarls' lethal axes. Then it is over. A strange silence falls across the clearing. Suddenly you feel very tired.

◊ Go to 77.

You nod to your bodyguards and give them permission to attack. The mighty warriors surge forward and charge violently up the slope. Suddenly you are left feeling very alone. Your bodyguard has been within touching distance of you for most of the day, and without the knights' protection you suddenly feel vulnerable.

Without thinking, you push your spurs into the flanks of your horse and spring forward to join your men. The wind whistles through your helmet as you race up the slope. You soon find your bodyguard who have come to a halt at the top of the slope.

◊ Go to 68.

88 Rating: Great General

You have performed as well as William the Conqueror did in 1066. The death of King Harold, and so many of his men, means that the way is clear for you to take control of England. This will be made easier by the fact that so many of the English warlords have died today. There is simply no one left to gather an army to rise against your rule.

You have shown all the qualities needed to be a great general. You have made the correct decisions, or been lucky when making the wrong choices. You have fought well and showed a ruthless streak when required. You clearly understand how to use your troops to the best effect, when to take advice and when to ignore your commanders.

◊ *Go to 57 to discover what really happened at the Battle of Hastings…*

---

89 You pass the order to Eustace and Bishop Odo to give your men some rest. It is close to midday and the autumn sun is high in the sky.

You send your commanders out to talk to their men, and they pass amongst them chatting – reassuring them – telling them to rest and regain their energy. You glance up the slope, where the English are also resting, and can clearly see King Harold striding amongst his men.

You decide to take the chance to talk to your men and lower yourself from your horse. The Normans in the centre and the French on the right still look strong. However, the Bretons on the left are another matter. The retreat and scrap with the English has taken its toll, and many Bretons are injured. You watch Alan Fergant walk amongst his men. He seems calm, though he has a bloody bandage strapped to his left arm.

You thoughts turn to the morning's battle. You recall that as the Bretons retreated, the undisciplined English fyrds were unable to resist the temptation to attack. Though the Bretons were nearly beaten, once the retreat had been stopped, many English fyrds were killed as they tried to return to their positions on the hill. If somehow you could trick the English into thinking your warriors were again retreating, then perhaps you might be able to lure some more of the fyrds out.

Your thoughts are broken by your half-brother Odo. He has returned to your side and looks refreshed. You explain your idea for a feint attack – using your cavalry to fake an attack on the English to lure warriors from behind the shield wall. Then your knights could quickly swing about and cut them down. Odo sits quietly as you speak. His eyes are cast towards the ground, rolling his mace in his hands.

At last he looks up and speaks, "Brother, I understand what you ask of your men, but the feint attack is a risky tactic. If it was not to work your knights would be cut down." Odo is wise, but he is a man of God before a warrior.

◊ *If you trust Odo's advice and think you should carry on without using a feint attack, move on to 39.*

◊ *If you trust your own feelings and wish to order your cavalry to prepare for a feint attack, then go to 7.*

You are still holding the broken weapon when you emerge into another, larger, clearing in the trees. At one end, a group of about twenty English warriors have gathered together to make a last stand. The group contains mostly housecarls armed with axes, but also fyrds armed with swords and even a couple of archers. They are gathered behind a large dip in the ground, possibly caused by a stream. The undergrowth around the English is very thick and to attack them your men will have to climb across the dip and fight up the slope on which they are positioned.

At the other end of the clearing, away from the English, you see about sixty of your men. As you examine them a noble figure appears from the throng. It is Eustace. Seeing you, he spurs his horse over to your position, the smile on his face showing that he is pleased to see you.

◊ *If you wish to talk to Eustace about the group of English, go to 23.*

◊ *If you have no time for chit-chat and wish to see the battle over, order the retreat at 42.*

You move to the nearest knight and ask if you can use his lance. He is honoured. You know the lance is more practical for the bloody murder in hand. It is a long wooden spear, light and flexible, an ideal killing weapon for the fleeing English.

Once again you signal your men to follow. As you re-enter the forest you can hear the sound of fighting to your left. You wheel your horse round and instinctively your knights follow, picking their way skilfully between the trees. You couch the lance under your arm and adjust your weight in the saddle. You have used the lance many times before, but mostly for hunting and skewering wild boars in Normandy. As you ride, this feels very similar.

A group of three English fyrds suddenly emerge from the trees to your right and you shift your weight slightly, nudging the horse in their direction. They are running along a rough path. In their haste to escape they have thrown away their shields and helmets, and are left with simply their swords. As you pass the first man you dip the tip of the lance, catching him squarely in the back. The momentum of your horse's movement takes you away from the man and you let the lance come free. The second fyrd turns as you come close, raising his sword. Despite his movement your lance pierces his chest. The weight of the impact twists your body, but you keep hold of the lance by yanking it free. The third fyrd is more of a problem. He has stopped running and turned to face you. Your horse is moving fast, but just as you lean forward to thrust your spear into him, he turns his body. He skilfully slashes at your weapon, breaking the shaft of the lance. You are unable to stop and rush past, leaving him far behind. You are now deep in the woods.

◊ *To push on, move to 90.*

◊ *If you feel you have strayed too far from the battlefield and are ready to stop fighting, go to 42.*

92 You have great faith in Alan Fergant and his Breton warriors, and watch the fight from the safety of your mound. However, many English warriors are flooding down the hill to join the fight. The Bretons are becoming outnumbered and they have been pushed together to fight in one group. In the centre Alan Fergant battles on. As each minute passes more Bretons are killed.

All across the hillside your troops have now pulled back from the English line and many of the men are watching the Bretons. You realise that you must react. You look around desperately for one of your commanders – Odo or Eustace. A sense of panic is building in you and your men.

Suddenly the English burst into action. A huge roar erupts from the housecarls as they charge from behind the shield wall with axes swinging. They smash into your Norman warriors. Though your Norman infantry are skilled fighters, the shock of the housecarl attack is too much and almost immediately they turn and flee. The French to the right of the Normans realise what has happened, and they too break and run. You can do nothing, all is lost. All you can hope for now is that you can escape and live to fight another day.

◊ *For you the Battle of Hastings is over. Go to 11 to* *discover your fate.*

93 As you move your horse through the crowd, you see a tall English warrior. He is not far away and suddenly stops fighting when he sees you. Then, with a flash of anger, he throws his spear towards you. It slams into the flank of your horse.

Your horse falls, and you twist from your saddle and scramble to your feet. You just manage to get your sword free before the warrior is upon you. Using your sword, you block his strike. In a sweeping motion he brings his sword under your guard. You easily step out of the way and thrust your blade into the soft flesh of his stomach. You step away as he slumps to the ground and leave him to die a slow, bloody death.

You're glancing around for another horse, when a magnificent knight appears from the crowd. It is Eustace. Anger flushes your face as you realise he has disobeyed your order to steady his men.

He rushes to your side

"Sire, take my mount, I will find another."

You're loath to accept Eustace's offer, but the battle is more important than your pride. You spring into the saddle.

◊ *To return to the centre to take command of your army, go to 95.*

◊ *If you feel you can do more good here and wish to keep fighting, then go to 34.*

The rain of arrows starts to slow and then eventually stops. You look down to the archers. Your men look confused, some are glancing in your direction shaking their heads.

You push your feet into the side of your horse and spring forward, looking for the leader of your archers. He is close by, surrounded by his men. As you ride up you draw your sword and scream at him to continue firing. The leader looks sternly in your direction, with anger in his eyes. You tighten the grip on your sword, ready to strike him down. However, he is not stupid and slowly turns to give the word for his men to continue firing.

As you ride away, you feel your anger slipping from your body. By the time you have returned to your command position you are calm. You turn to survey the battle. Immediately you see that the archers have disobeyed your orders. The arrows are not falling on the mass of fighting men, but instead are flying high over the ranks into the English behind. You are about to react, when you feel a smile creeping onto your lips. The archers have not really disobeyed your order. You instructed them to shoot at the English and that is what is happening. The fact that they are avoiding their own men and killing English instead is probably for the best anyway.

◊ *Go to 65.*

The fight on the left wing has been hard and as you ride back to the centre you feel very tired. As you glance around, slowly taking in the scene on the hill, you realise something is wrong. In every direction you can see your men retreating. When you raced to help the Bretons your men had been pushed back from the English shield wall. They looked unsteady, but you had confidence in your men and commanders. It was a mistake! Your army is now in full retreat. All across the slope you can see your warriors racing towards the valley.

You turn your attention to the English. They are no longer formed in a solid shield wall. Instead, they have broken from their line and begun to pursue your men. The situation in the valley is no better. Some of your warriors are running for their lives. However, others have formed into small groups and are fighting desperately as the English surge forward.

As you struggle to decide what to do, your half-brother Odo appears from the crowd. He is no longer mounted and is running to your position. You are glad to see him. Almost at the same time you see Eustace racing on a horse from your right. The battle is slipping from your hands.

◊ *To send your commanders to try to stop the retreat, act now by going to 6.*

◊ *To keep them at your side, go to 4.*

You pass the word for the archers to shoot their arrows into the mass of fighting men at the top of the slope. As the order is passed to the men, some turn in your direction, a look of confusion in their eyes. Finally, the archers prepare for the first volley.

Slowly the archers draw their bows, the strings being held firmly to their chests. They lift the point of the arrow, aiming high into the sky. The sun is low, dipping to tree top level over your left shoulder, and is in the eyes of the English troops.

The archers release the strings and the arrows spring into the air with a whoosh. The black cloud rises into the sky, before falling on the heads of the troops fighting on the lip of the slope. The archers quickly reload and shoot again and again and again.

Almost immediately you realise your mistake. You watch with horror as arrows rain down onto the mass of men, piercing bodies and puncturing helmets. Hundreds of warriors drop to the ground dead or screaming in pain. However, it is not just the English who are hit. Many of your men have become intermingled with the enemy and they too are being killed and wounded.

◊ *To order the archers to continue firing into the front rank, go to 94.*

◊ *If you feel they would be better firing into the ranks behind, go now to 79.*

You spur your horse forward heading directly for
Harold. Eustace reacts first and follows closely,
lance held low. Two other knights also react and
head towards the King with their lances ready.

There are about eleven housecarls guarding the
injured King. Yet, they are no match for you and
your knights. The first four housecarls are killed
instantly as you plunge into their group.

You reach the King first and swing your sword
powerfully into his chest. You can feel the rings in
his armour split and the sharp blade meeting royal
flesh. You are then past Harold as the momentum
of your horse carries you forward. Pulling hard
on your horse's reins, you try to swing the mount
back for a second blow. Eustace is upon Harold,
his lance held low. The speed of his charge thrusts
the point of the lance into the King's side, ripping
the flesh. The second knight's lance hits home
a moment later, catching the King's arm and
wrenching the muscle from the bone. The last
knight deals a blow deep into Harold's stomach.

Eustace then dismounts, jumping smoothly
to the ground. Dropping his lance, he whips
his sword from its scabbard and plunges it into
the body of the King. The other knights follow
Eustace's example. You remain on your horse.

You glance at Eustace and he smiles weakly.
You turn your attention back to King Harold. It is

then that you notice that one of his legs is missing! You glance around quickly. To your right one of your knights is trying to remount his horse, in his left hand he holds his sword, while in his right he carries the leg of the King. You shout for him to stop, but your voice is lost, and before you can move he is on his mount and riding back towards the Norman line. The royal leg is tucked firmly under his arm.

You turn to Eustace and he points back the way that you came. You see that your men have now pushed their way onto the top of the hill. Hundreds of Normans stand in a mass. Eustace spurs his horse in their direction and you follow. It only takes a few minutes to reach the safety of your men, but for once you are glad of Eustace's quick thinking. The battle is changing.

◊ *To order all of your men on the ridge to attack and drive the English from the battlefield, go to 68.*

◊ *If you wish to wait a moment and examine the situation more closely, go to 40.*

---

98 You order the little man to pass out the arrows. He quickly shuffles away without another word.

Soon you see many dirty peasants scuttling about the battlefield with rolls of arrows tucked under their arms. It is not long before your archers are ready for action, poised at the base of the slope, awaiting your orders. You spur your horse towards the commander of the archers.

◊ *To order your archers to shoot into the mass of fighting warriors at the lip of the hill, go to 96.*

◊ *To order them to shoot over the fighting men into the English behind the line, go to 79.*

It has been a long and hard day, and you are surrounded by death and destruction. The small hill is strewn with the bodies of the dead and the cries of the injured. Your men are tired and the day is won. You turn to your knights and pass the order to stop fighting. The word soon spreads and your army stops chasing the enemy. Your men are exhausted, hungry and thirsty. It is not long before your tired men have grouped together and started small fires, making hot food and drink. The battle is over and you have won. The first part of your invasion is a success.

◊ *Congratulations! You have defeated the English. However, your victory is not complete. Go to 71 to discover your fate.*

Odo rides towards you, still smiling. You greet your half-brother as he speaks.

"The English are fools, look at them panic. We should attack again." You consider his words and quickly nod in agreement. Odo races away to instruct the Norman knights.

Your gaze returns to the top of the slope. All along the line, men continue to fight for you. Bodies have begun to pile up. All across the battlefield blood, weapons and armour are scattered on the ground. Yet, the English remain firm. You guess that you have killed many of their men and you suspect that their line looks shorter, but you cannot be sure. However, the shield wall remains intact.

Once again you watch your knights ride up the hill to the shield wall. And once again they race away, waiting for the English to follow. Yet, this time it is different. The English laugh and wave their weapons at the knights. The feint attack will not work again.

It is getting late and the sun is sitting low in the sky. As you consider your next move, you see a strange-looking man walking towards you. He has a long beard, but he is only as tall as a child. He lifts his hand in the air and calls out your name.

◊ *To talk to the man, go to 10.*

◊ *If you feel the man can only bring trouble, then turn to 30.*

BATTLE BOOKS
BEHIND THE SCENES

The author: GARY SMAILES

I decided to write the Battle Books series after
becoming really annoyed that someone had
not already got off their backsides and written
them for me. You see, battles are just so great
to read about – all the weapons and action – in
fact, I don't understand why there aren't more
books about them…

I live on the Wirral, which many years ago
was inhabited by real-life Vikings. Sometimes,
when I'm writing and I get stuck, I go out for
a walk with my (stinky) dog. I imagine I'm
part of a Viking army defending my land.

If I could have three wishes, one would be
that I was a Viking, and the other would be
to own a Viking longboat. The third would be
that my dog didn't smell so much!

The artist: OLLIE CUTHBERTSON

Hi, I'm Ollie and I drew the artwork in *Battle Books: Hastings*. I love capturing the action in a battle. Sometimes it's a whole cavalry unit, other times it could be just a single warrior, like the artwork below.

I draw in two main stages for Battle Books. First I create a rough sketch, then I make changes and draw the final piece in ink, with some grey fill.

ROUGH   FINAL

The piece above is from paragraph 68. At first I included William's sword arm at the bottom, but this didn't give the housecarl axeman enough room. For the final I changed his position, left out William's sword arm and moved the horse. This gave the piece much more tension; capturing the moment just before the housecarl swings his axe down. Duck!

BATTLE BOOKS

Take up your weapons and prepare to fight your own battle...

978 1 4451 0112 5

978 1 4451 0113 2

978 1 4451 0114 9

978 1 4451 0115 6